THE Dandy

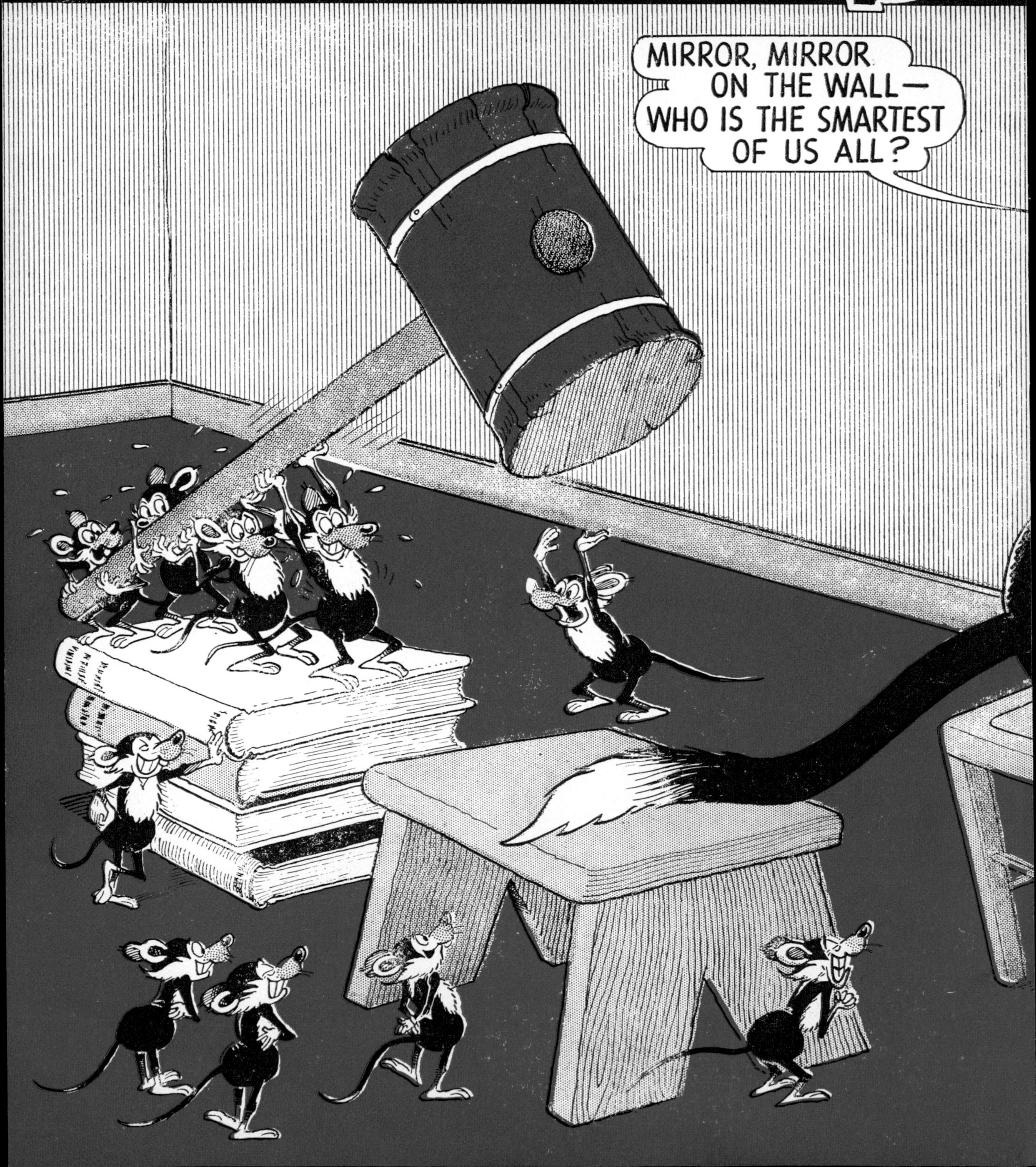

BOOK

This book belongs to

NAME _____

ADDRESS _____

_____

_____

_____

Printed and Published by D. C. Thomson & Co., Ltd., Dundee and London.

Blundering BEN

THE Bentley Boys were lucky lads. They had the best gang hut you ever saw, and they were proud of it. Once, it had been a shepherd's cottage, and it was a sturdy building that could withstand wind and rain and, above all, raids from Whacker Wagstaffe's gang.

One winter's morning Tony Bentley, the leader of the gang, arrived at the cottage door with his cousin Ben from Canada. Ben was the same age as Tony, but so much smaller that his English cousin had doubts about him. What would the gang think of such a shorty?

The all-clear was given and the door swung open. But it was just as Tony had feared. The reception his cousin got was cool. Ben didn't look as though he would be much good in a tussle with Wagstaffe's lot, and that was what counted.

HOWDY, BOYS!

HIYA, GANG! MEET MY COUSIN, BEN. HE'S ALL THE WAY FROM CANADA!

ER—HULLO!

One lad had a large tin of peaches. It would make a super feast—if only they could open the tin. Eager to get in the good books, Ben offered to help.

I'VE GOT A SUPER GADGET FOR OPENING TINS. I'LL FETCH IT FROM MY BICYCLE!

Ben dashed out and rummaged in his saddle bag. He didn't see a nasty customer creep up behind him. It was Whacker.

NOW WHERE'S THAT GADGET GOT TO?

HULLO! WHAT DO I SPY WITH MY GREEDY LITTLE EYE?

Whacker pounced. There was a quick scuffle as he grabbed the tin of peaches and stifled Ben's cry.

MMM!

THIS BIG TIN IS TOO HEAVY FOR A LITTLE GUY LIKE YOU! LET ME CARRY IT FOR YOU!

But Whacker didn't take part in the skirmish. The greedy double-crosser sneaked off to gobble all he could on his own.

HEE-HEE! I CAN HARDLY WAIT TO GET MY TEETH INTO THESE PEACHES!

Whacker's first problem was how to open the tin. A sharp tap with a big stone drove his opener through the lid.

Little did he know that Ben had passed unharmed through the ambush and had tracked him down!

Armed with a piece of sacking, the Canadian boy crept up behind Whacker with all the stealth of a wild animal.

Before Whacker could make a move, Ben whisked the sack over the rotter's head and shoulders. Too bad that the half-open tin was upset by Whacker's flying hoof!

GOT YOU!

HELP!

Leaving Whacker to struggle free, Ben scampered off with what was left of the peaches.

When Ben met up with the Bentley Boys, he found them looking in a sorry state. Every man jack had taken a biffing from Whacker's ambushers.

That was bad enough. But when the Bentley Boys found half their peaches gone—!

The lads hurried back to their gang hut. They were expecting more trouble. Whacker and his gang would follow for sure, and when Ben heard this, he looked round thoughtfully.

Ben had often helped his Dad set traps in Canada. So while the others went on ahead, Ben got to work.

It didn't take long for Ben to set up the trap, and he was mighty pleased with it. But he felt there should be a further safety measure.

At last there was a chance to dish out the peaches. Then, just as the first mouthful was swallowed, there was a wild yell from outside.

YEEAARGH!

WHAT ON EARTH WAS THAT?

The gang dashed outside, and to their dismay they found the two sentries caught in Ben's trap.

YOU AND YOUR BRIGHT IDEAS!

HELP!

OH, NO!

Even worse, there was no time to cut them down, for Whacker's gang was charging over the hill.

THERE THEY ARE! GET THEM!

RUN FOR IT!

But Ben had made other secret plans. From behind the gang hut he rolled out a monster snowball.

GOOD JOB I PREPARED THIS SNOWBALL!

Ben sent the thumping great ball of snow trundling towards the Whacker gang.

LOOK OUT, LADS, OR WE'LL BE FLATTENED!

But the best laid plans of poor Ben were going oft astray. The snowball hit a ridge of snow, veered away from Whacker's gang and thundered into the Bentley Boys, knocking them over like ninepins.

OOF!

HELP!

YAHOO!

The Canadian boy had done what the Whacker gang had never managed to do. With hidden bear traps and a monster snowball he had put the whole Bentley gang out of action.

But the Bentley Boys managed to scramble into the safety of their hut before Whacker's gang could grab them. By this time Ben was as popular as a porcupine at a balloon blowing contest.

KEEP OUT!

ME YOU! BUZZ OF

YOUR BRIGHT IDEAS HAVEN'T HALF LANDED US IN THE SOUP!

But all was not lost. Ben spotted a hose under the sink, and that set him thinking fast. First he buckled on his ice skates and then he jammed the hose on the cold water tap.

As the Bentley Boys stared, the Canadian boy pushed the hose through the window, turned on the water and dashed outside.

CRUMBS! WHERE'S HE OFF TO NOW?

Whacker's mob were closing in when Ben jerked up the hose and whisked it back and forth. SWOOSH! The jet of water stopped the attackers in their tracks.

Furious, the drenched bullies charged after Ben. But the Canadian boy had planned well. He turned away towards a frozen pond. Hampered by his skates, he could only hobble. Would he make it?

Ben made it—though only by a whisker! But as soon as his skates hit the ice, he zoomed forward like a greyhound leaving its trap.

The bullies came skidding on to the ice after the Canadian boy. Then all of a sudden Ben gave a start. He was heading straight for a patch of thin ice! Was another of his bright ideas about to go wrong?

But the Bentley Boys had had enough of this Canadian clown. He had done more damage than all the Whacker gang put together, and they meant to give Ben what for.

WE'VE HAD ENOUGH OF YOU! GRAB HIM!

NOW JUST A MINUTE, YOU GUYS! DON'T BE HASTY!

Saved by the bell! The Bentley Boys were on the point of grabbing Ben when they saw Whacker and his gang scrambling out of the freezing water.

BRRR!

WELL, HOW ABOUT THAT? HE'S DEALT WITH THE WHACKER MOB SINGLE-HANDED!

GANG RULE

THREE CHEERS FOR BEN! HIP-HIP-HURRAY!

Ben had made good at last. He was not just welcomed as a new pal but as a hero, too. And he was even more popular when he brought along a crate of fruity drinks to serve out amongst the Bentley Boys.

FRUITO FRUIT DRINK CO PRODUCE of CANADA

BAH! IT'S LANDED IN THE CANAL!

SPLOOSH!

NEVER MIND! I'VE TIED A ROPE TO A DART, AND HARPOONED THE BOARD.

OH, NO! HERE COMES TEACHER AGAIN! I'D BETTER PULL THE BOARD IN QUICK.

TUG!

DID YOU SEE A DART-BOARD ROLL THIS WAY, SMASHER?

A DARTBOARD, SIR? THAT'S A FUNNY THING TO SEE ROLLING ALONG THE ROAD!

WHUMP!

OH, HO!

OOF!

COME ON, SMASHER—I'M TAKING YOU TO SEE YOUR DAD!

YOWCH!

TUG!

WHAT'S HE DONE?

EVERYTHING BUT HIS HOMEWORK, I'LL BET.

OOER!

THEY'RE WORKING SOMETHING OUT AND I BET IT'S A PUNISH-MENT FOR ME.

RIGHT! WE'RE GOING TO HAVE A GAME OF DARTS AND YOU CAN JOIN IN, SMASHER.

GOSH! SMASHING!

BUT—

NOT SO SMASHING! THEY'VE ONLY ALLOWED ME TO KEEP SCORE— AND THAT'S WORSE THAN DOING SUMS!

IF YOU MAKE A MISTAKE AND MAKE ME LOSE, SMASHER, YOU'RE FOR IT!

CLUNK!

THROW!

DAD	TEACHER
301	301
29	27

AND THERE WILL BE A HUNDRED LINES FOR EVERY MISTAKE YOU MAKE IN MY SCORE!

Dirty DICK

FANCY HAVING ALL THESE STICKY SWEETS AND BEING SCARED TO EAT THEM! BUT I DAREN'T GET MY FACE MESSED UP OR MUM WILL HALF KILL ME!

STICKY TOFFEE

I'LL HAVE THOSE SWEETS, DICK!

OO-ER! IT'S BULLY BATES!

HAND THEM OVER OR I'LL SEE YOUR FACE GETS MESSED UP—WITH MY FIST!

OOER!

I HEARD THAT, BATES! IF DICK GETS MESSED UP AT ALL TODAY, I'LL REPORT YOU TO YOUR DAD!

OO!

THANKS, CONSTABLE JONES.

SO—

COAL YARD

NOW'S MY CHANCE TO PAY OFF SOME OLD SCORES! SOOTY SMITH FOR A START!

WHAT'S THE GAME?

OUT OF THE WAY, DICK! IF YOU GET DIRTY I'LL GET THE BLAME!

TAKE THAT!

SOOT

OO, TA, BULLY BATES!

LOOK! THE GASWORKS GANG! HEY! DO YOU CISSIES WANT A FIGHT?

BAH! LEAVE DICK ALONE AND FIGHT ME, YOU BLOCKHEADS!

SURE, BATES, WE DON'T MIND—WE'LL FIGHT ANYBODY!

HO-HO! THAT WAS FUN! RECKON I'LL HAVE A SWEET NOW!

OH, NO!

BACK HOME—

DICK! YOU'RE FOR IT!

DON'T PUNISH HIM, MISSUS. IF HE GOT MESSED UP IT WAS ANOTHER LAD TO BLAME, AND HE'LL BE FOR IT WHEN I TELL HIS DAD!

DON'T BOTHER, P.C. JONES. HIS DAD'S GOT THE RIGHT IDEA ALREADY!

I'LL TEACH YOU NOT TO COME HOME IN SUCH A MESS AGAIN, MY LAD!

YUMMY! WHO WOULD HAVE GUESSED I COULD HAVE AS MUCH FUN WITH ONE PACKET OF SWEETS?

I'M AN *INK*Y CHAP, YOU KNOW! I EVEN HAVE *INK* IN MY NICKNAME—W*INK*ER. LOTS OF OTHER WORDS HAVE *INK* IN THEM, IF YOU TH*INK* ABOUT IT—AND THERE'S ONE FOR A START! SEE HOW MANY YOU CAN FIND, AND IF YOU LOOK AT MY PICTURE CLUES YOU'LL GET AN *INK*LING (OOPS! ANOTHER ONE!) ABOUT ALL THE WORDS I HAVE DISCOVERED.

FULL LIST OF ANSWERS ON PAGE **48**, BUT DON'T LOOK AT IT UNTIL YOU'VE HAD A GO!

7

POTS AND PANS TO MEND! KNIVES TO GRIND!

8

9

VELLY EASY ONE THIS— IT'S MY NICKNAME!

13

MY FUR COAT WAS VERY EXPENSIVE!

SOLD

14

A CHAIN IS AS STRONG AS ITS WEAKEST ONE!

15

SKATES FOR HIRE

19

SO WHAT? YOU CALL IT THAT, I CALL IT THE - - - - - !

TOWN JAIL

20

KY PUZZLE

1. O BOY, AM I THIRSTY? GLUG-GLUG!

2. YOU FIND THEM ON THE ROCKS, AND EAT THEM WITH A PIN!

3. OO, LOOK! A CASKET FULL OF - - - - - - - !

4. THE WORD YOU WANT DESCRIBES THE WAY THIS CAT IS MOVING.

5. ROTTEN EGGS

6. OO-ER! I DIDN'T KNOW MY JERSEY WAS GOING TO DO THIS! DUCK POND

10. WHAT A SILLY PICTURE. IT'S ONLY PAINTED IN ONE COLOUR!

11. IT'S WHAT MY HAIR IS!

12. OY! DON'T STAND ON THE - - - - - - OF THAT CLIFF! DANGER

16. I HOPE THE GUV'NOR KNOWS WHERE WE'RE GOING — I CAN'T SEE A THING!

17. IT'S LIKE THE STAR IN THE NURSERY RHYME, DADDY.

18. SILENCE DURING EXAM. QUESTIONS

21. I CAN SWIM, MY FEET ARE TOUCHING THE BOTTOM AND I'M WEARING A LIFEBELT — SO I'M PRACTICALLY - - - - - - - - !

22. I'M 99 NEXT BIRTHDAY, SO IT'S NO WONDER MY FACE IS FULL OF 'EM!

23. ONE OF THESE GLASSES OF LIQUID IS SALTY, BUT THE OTHER IS - - - - - - - !

GREEDY PIGG

HEE-HEE! LOOK AT THEM HIDING THEIR GOODIES IN THEIR DESKS!

NOW TO GET RID OF THE BOYS SO THAT I CAN GRAB THE EATS!

OH, BOY! THE BOYS ARE TAKING LOTS OF SWEETS AND GOODIES INTO CLASS. I CAN HARDLY WAIT TO GET MY HANDS ON THEM AND SCOFF THEM MYSELF!

GOOD MORNING, BOYS! SHOW ME YOUR HANDS TO SEE THAT THEY'RE ALL CLEAN!

JUST AS I THOUGHT—THEY'RE ALL VERY DIRTY!

OFF YOU GO AND WASH YOURSELVES!

THAT'S GOT RID OF THEM ALL! NOW FOR THE GRUB!

UGH—INK!

BAH! THE YOUNG SCAMP HAD RIGGED UP A TRAP! I'LL TRY THESE NEXT DESKS!

THUD

WHAM

YEEAARGH!

YIPPEE! NOW WE CAN EAT OUR GRUB IN PEACE!

GROAN!

Korky the Cat

TWO LETTERS FOR YOU, KORKY.

OH, THANKS!

KORKY HARLOW BLOCK

FANCY THAT! TWO INVITATIONS TO TWO PARTIES, BOTH ON THE SAME DAY— AND BOTH IN THE SAME BLOCK!

A PARTY INVITATION

ONE IS IN THE GROUND FLOOR FLAT, AND THE OTHER IN THE FLAT ABOVE—SO I'VE FIXED THIS BUCKET ON A PULLEY.

HERE YOU ARE, KORKY!

SEE HOW I CAN PULL MYSELF UP FOR MY SHARE OF YOUR PARTY GRUB!

THAT WAS GOOD! NOW I'LL LOWER MYSELF DOWN FOR A HELPING FROM THE DOWNSTAIRS PARTY.

ALL FOR YOU, KORKY!

HERE'S MORE FOR YOU, KORKY!

COMING UP! GOSH! I'M GETTING FULL!

ON IT GOES! UGH! GROOGH!

JUST MAKE SURE IT'S STUCK PROPERLY! OOH!

THANKS FOR YOUR HELP, CHIPS! BETTER GET IT AWAY—THE POSTMAN WILL BE ALONG SOON! GRR!

TAKE THAT, YOU ROTTER! YEOWCH! BOOT!

HELP! MY ARM'S STUCK! HEE-HEE! SERVES YOU RIGHT!

GET ME OUT! THE POSTMAN WILL BE ALONG ANY SECOND! WELL, I THINK I MIGHT BE ABLE TO HELP!

HOLD STILL! HEY! WHAT ARE YOU DOING?

YAAGH! ITCHING POWDER! THAT'S RIGHT—AND IT DID THE TRICK!

OOF! ARRGH! G.P.O. CRASH!

WHEN YOU'VE PICKED 'EM ALL UP, WE'LL GO AND SEE WHAT YOUR FATHER WILL THINK YOU WERE UP TO WITH YOUR ARM STUCK IN THE BOX. TRYING TO PINCH THE MAIL, I RECKON! OH, NO! HO-HO! BET BEEFY WISHES HE COULD POST HIMSELF TO TIMBUCTOO!

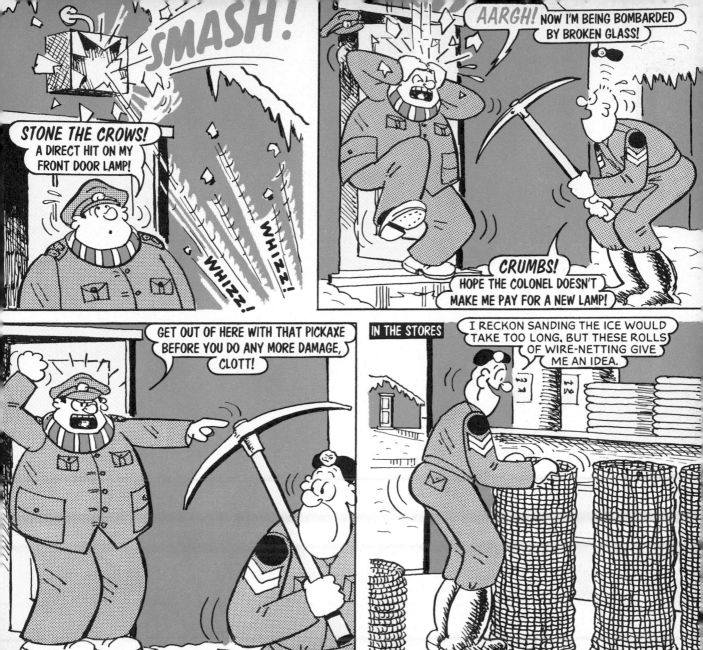

SMASH!

STONE THE CROWS! A DIRECT HIT ON MY FRONT DOOR LAMP!

WHIZZ!

WHIZZ!

AARGH! NOW I'M BEING BOMBARDED BY BROKEN GLASS!

CRUMBS! HOPE THE COLONEL DOESN'T MAKE ME PAY FOR A NEW LAMP!

GET OUT OF HERE WITH THAT PICKAXE BEFORE YOU DO ANY MORE DAMAGE, CLOTT!

IN THE STORES

I RECKON SANDING THE ICE WOULD TAKE TOO LONG, BUT THESE ROLLS OF WIRE-NETTING GIVE ME AN IDEA.

THE WIRE IS FREEZING TO THE GROUND AND THAT IS HOLDING IT FLAT.

THERE YOU ARE, SIR! YOUR PATH IS QUITE SAFE TO WALK ON NOW!

I'LL TRY A FEW STEPS ON IT.

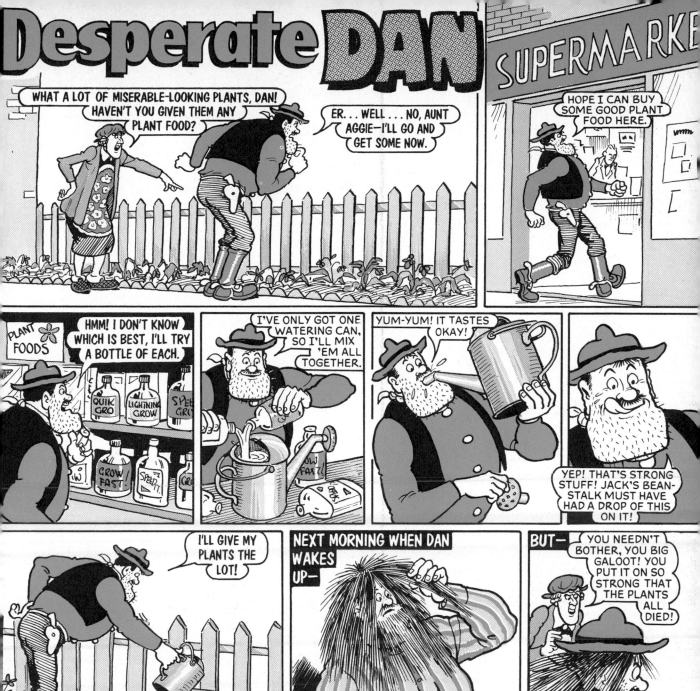

BATTY BALLADS

A prospector both daring and bold,
Last November went panning for gold.
At the end of the day,
He had three tons of clay,
Four fish, seven boots and a cold.

There was a prim lady called Bessie,
Who went to the loch to see Nessie.
She fell in the mud,
With a terrible thud,
And so Nessie saw Bessie all messy.

There was a young man from Tobruk,
Who fancied himself as a crook.
On his very first raid,
The mistake that he made
Was to sign the visitors' book.

A scatty young shopper from Scropping
Wore antlers each time he went shopping.
"The reason," said he,
"Is quite plain to see,
It stops all my parcels from dropping!"

There was a young cricketer from Neath,
While batting, got hit in the teeth.
He spat out a molar,
And said to the bowler,
"A little more care if you pleath!"

A funny young fellow called Glugg,
Invented a bottomless mug.
When he started to sip
It ran down his lip,
And made a big stain on the rug.

ANSWERS TO WINKER'S INKY PUZZLE

(See pages 24-25)

1–Drink, 2–Winkles, 3–Trinkets, 4–Slinking, 5–Stink, 6–Shrink, 7–Sink, 8–Tinker, 9–Kink, 10–Pink, 11–Crinkly, 12–Brink, 13–Chink, 14–Mink, 15–Link, 16–Blinkers, 17–Twinkling, 18–Thinking, 19–Rink, 20–Clink, 21–Unsinkable, 22–Wrinkles, 23–Drinkable.

The SMASHER

DAD BOUGHT A LOAD OF OLD PADLOCKS IN A SALE, AND HE'S USING THEM TO LOCK UP ALL THE CUPBOARDS. I CAN'T GET INTO THE PANTRY, OR EVEN INTO MY TOY CUPBOARD!

I CAN'T GET MY TOYS OUT, SO I'LL JUST HAVE SOME FUN WITH THESE PADLOCKS.

THERE'S THE PARK ROAD GANG, I BET THEY'RE PLANNING AN ATTACK ON OUR GANG HUT. SO I'LL FIX THEM!

GANG HUT

A LITTLE LATER—

HEY! LET US OUT!

HO-HO! THESE PADLOCKS ARE SMASHING!

FURTHER ON—

LOOK! THERE'S SMASHER AND HE HASN'T GOT HIS CATTY—

WOW! FOUR TO ONE!

TIME TO GO!

AFTER HIM!

HE MUST BE HIDING IN THAT HUT. WE'LL GET HIM NOW!

HEE-HEE! NOW'S MY CHANCE!

WHERE IS HE?

BAH! WE'RE LOCKED IN!

HAW-HAW! YOU'D DO BETTER TO LEAVE THE SMASHER ALONE, LADS!

AT SCHOOL—

OH, DEAR! I FORGOT TO DO MY HOMEWORK LAST NIGHT. GOOD JOB I'M FIRST IN CLASS.

EEK! A PADLOCK ON THE CANE CUPBOARD! HOW DID THAT GET THERE?

SHAKE!

INK

URGH!

COME ALONG, SMASHER. I KNOW IT MUST HAVE BEEN YOU BECAUSE NO ONE ELSE HAS TURNED UP TODAY.

BAH! THAT'S BECAUSE I LOCKED THEM ALL UP!

STAFF ROOM

BULLY BEEF and CHIPS

"HERE'S A LITTLE PRESENT FOR YOU, BULLY BEEF!"

"GOSH, THANKS, AUNT MAUD! I LOVE GETTING PRESENTS!"

"WHAT A LOVELY T-SHIRT! PUT IT ON BEFORE YOU GO OUT TO PLAY!"

"B-BUT, MA, I'M TOO OLD FOR TEDDY-BEAR T-SHIRTS!"

"BAH! MA SAID SHE WOULDN'T LET ME OUT UNLESS I PUT THIS SOPPY THING ON!"

"HO-HO! LOOK AT TEDDY-BEAR BEEF!"

"GURR!"

"IF YOU THINK THAT TEDDY-BEAR'S FUNNY, LET'S SEE YOU LAUGH AT THIS BEAR-HUG!"

"OOF!"

CRUSH!

"NOW, WHAT HAVE WE GOT IN HERE?"

"GASP!"

"AH—HONEY! BEARS LIKE HONEY!"

HONEY

"—AND SO DO I!"

"BAH!"

When Charley arrived at his gang hut there were some funny sights to greet him. All his pals were togged out in armour, too, and some of the outfits weren't half odd.

I'M INVINCIBLE IN THIS OUTFIT, CHARLEY!

HO-HO! YOU LOOK LIKE A WALKING CAN OF BEEF, TUBBY!

WE'LL MURDER THE HAWK STREET GANG TODAY, BRASSNECK.

TEE-HEE!

With all this kidding going on, no one noticed a sneaky schoolboy called Swotty Watt spying.

HUH! SO THAT LOT THINK THEY'RE TOUGH? WELL, I'LL SOON SCATTER THEM.

Swotty's Dad was a professor, and he had built a secret radio gadget which enabled Swotty to take control of Brassneck. All he need do to cause trouble was to press a switch.

GOSH!

WHAT'S UP WITH BRASSNECK ALL OF A SUDDEN?

DUNNO. MAYBE HE NEEDS OILING.

WHIRR!

CLANK!

The funny metal armour wasn't much use as Brassneck attacked with a length of piping. Charley and his chums were driven off.

BLEEP! SCRAM, YOU TIN CAN FREAKS! HURRAH FOR SWOTTY WATT AND ENGLAND!

YAHOO!

RUN, LADS! HE'S GONE BONKERS!

EEK!

CLANG!

HELP! I CAN'T RUN IN THIS ARMOUR! I'LL HAVE TO GET IT OFF!

With no one left to stop him, Swotty raided the gang hut for grub and sat down for a tuck in and a laugh at a comic. He didn't dream he was making a big mistake.

Suddenly the toughs who had been creeping up sprang on the guzzler from all sides. Swotty was overpowered in a moment.

WHAT A LARK THIS IS!

SSH! QUIET, LADS. THERE'S ONE OF 'EM.

GOT HIM!

YIPPEE!

WE'LL TAKE THE SKUNK PRISONER.

WAIT TILL BRAND HEARS WE'VE GOT ONE OF HIS PALS.

Swotty was in a proper stew now, and it was his own fault. For these were members of the gang which Charley and his pals had donned their suits of armour to do battle with.

GOSH! FANCY THAT! THE HAWK STREET MOB HAVE CAPTURED SWOTTY.

THEY'RE WELCOME TO HIM.

QUICK MARCH AN' SHUT UP!

The idea of collecting a ransom to save Swotty brought roars of laughter from Charley and his pals.

HO-HO! WE'D GIVE 'EM THAT TO KEEP SWOTTY FOR GOOD!

RANSOM NOTE
HAND OVER SIX PIES IF YOU WANT YOUR PAL SET FREE.
Signed THE HAWK ST. GANG

But Brassneck was still under Swotty's control and his angry shout made Charley gasp.

But Brassneck didn't shut up. He grabbed a stick and herded Charley's pals in pursuit.

The pals could hardly believe it when they found themselves at the rival gang hut risking their necks to save a rotter.

Charley would have been even more surprised if he'd seen the toughs giggling at them — from behind a fence!

One mighty rush with the battering ram shattered the door, and the rammers charged inside.

Charley's yell was drowned as he plunged head first into cold water. The crafty toughs had expected an attack and laid this trap.

Charley was hopping mad now and ready for a real fight. But the Hawk Street horrors had another trick ready.

Brassneck held the angry lads back when he saw the fate the toughs had prepared for the skinny twerp.

GOSH! WE DAREN'T LET THEM HARM SWOTTY.

AW! WHY NOT?

SEE?

OH, MOTHER!

I HOPE THEY TRY SOMETHING.

Then the gang leader handed over a list that made Charley goggle. The toughs wanted an even bigger ransom now!

RIDICULOUS!

GOSH!

LIST OF RANSOM DEMANDS

What was worse, Brassneck was still anxious to save Swotty! He was ready to bash anyone who didn't obey him.

STEP ON IT! WE MUSTN'T LET THE SKINNY ONE DOWN!

B-BUT!

First thing on the ransom list was those pies—and Brassneck knew that Tubby Dawson's Mum always baked pies today.

COME ON, FATTY!

ER-OKAY! BUT I ONLY DARE TAKE ONE.

Tubby was true to his word—but he hadn't reckoned on the brass traitor having a plan of his own. Brassneck fired a pebble through his peashooter hooter.

GOT IT! NOW TO SCRAM—YOW!

The yell brought Tubby's Mum running, and that bulge under his jersey gave him away.

TUBBY! WHAT HAVE YOU GOT THERE? LET ME SEE!

ER—NOTHING, MUM!

For two fatties, Mum and Son could move pretty fast. Before the chase was over, Brassneck had snaffled the other pies.

HELP!

COME BACK, YOU PIE THIEF!

HEE-HEE!

Poor Tubby got the blame for this too, of course, but Brassneck didn't care. He had enough pies to please the Hawk Street guzzlers now.

I'LL SOON HAVE THE MIGHTY SWOTTY FREE!

YOW! DON'T WHACK ME AGAIN, MA! HE MADE ME DO IT!

Ice cream was wanted next, but Charley and his pals had only enough to buy one cone between them.

OOH! MUM WASN'T HALF MAD!

HAND OVER YOUR CASH, LADS!

BUT WE'RE ALL BROKE, YOU TIN TWIT!

Luigi Macaroni knew how to deal with cadgers.

ANY FREE ICE CREAM, MR MACARONI. IT'S TO HELP SWOTTY OUT.

CLEAR OFF!

But Brassneck knew how to deal with Luigi.

MY FRIENDS WILL CLEAN UP YOUR SHOP IF YOU GIVE US SOME.

WELL, OKAY!

Brassneck's deal meant a lot of hard work for Charley and his pals. They knew that if they didn't polish up the shop, they would be polished off by Brassneck!

GASP! PANT!

FANCY US WORKING LIKE THIS TO HELP SWOTTY! BAH!

PHEW!

IT'S A DISGRACE!

GET A MOVE ON, BOY. I'M THIRSTY.

THE METAL LAD SAID YOU WOULDN'T MIND CLEANING THE CELLAR TOO, BOYS!

SCRUB

When the cleaning work was done, the boys would have given anything for a cool ice. But — nothing doing!

The next item on the ransom list was a new football.

It was the last straw for Charley! He raced home ahead of his traitor pal and beat him to the cupboard for the ball.

What a chase there was now! Charley flew as fast as his legs would carry him, desperate to save his ball.

The tireless metal lad was catching up as Charley ran down a hill. Desperately Charley did a one-handed grab at a rope hanging from a tree.

There was only one chance for Charley now. Holding on tight, he swung himself off his feet and round the tree.

What a turnaround! Charley's weight carried him full circle, and with his feet outstretched, he came swinging at his treacherous chum from behind. Wham!

If Brassneck had been in a daft mood before, the fall knocked him crazier still. His electric brainbox spun.

ER—ARE YOU OKAY, BRASSNECK?

BLEEP-BLOOP! CLINKA-CLUNKA— DOODLE-DOO!

SORRY, PAL! BUT YOU'VE HAD THIS COMING TO YOU ALL MORNING!

WHIRL

BIFF!

WOW! EEYAAGH!

The metal maddie was knocked flying head over heels on to the rocks below.

Charley's troubles looked as if they were only beginning. Now his crazy pal came at him like a raging bull.

ROAR! SNORT!

EEK! HE'S DAFTER THAN EVER!

Only a last minute dodge saved Charley. Brassneck slammed head first into a tree!

OOF! GERLUNK!

WOW! THANK GOODNESS THAT WASN'T ME!

WHAM!

Charley could have jumped for joy, for the terrific blow was just what Brassneck needed. It brought him back to rights and out of the grip of Swotty's control box.

OOH! WHAT HAPPENED, CHARLEY? HOW DID WE GET DOWN HERE?

GOLLY! DON'T YOU REMEMBER ABOUT SAVING SWOTTY OR ANYTHING?

WHAT? WHO'D BE DAFT ENOUGH TO SAVE SWOTTY? WHAT ARE YOU TALKING ABOUT?

This was more like the Brassneck Charley and his pals knew. The brass boy rallied the lads round the gang standard.

Togged up in armour again, Charley led his pals in a magnificent death or glory charge upon the enemy.

The Hawk Street horrors were caught napping this time and were completely crushed under the terrific onslaught. The toughs had played lots of dirty tricks upon Charley and his pals in the past, and they paid for all that with a biffing they would never forget.

The surprise attack had prevented the toughs from carrying out their threat on Swotty. Look how the rotter grinned when he saw Brassneck approach.

But Swotty was in for a surprise, and no mistake!

YOU'RE GOING FOR A SAIL, SWOTTY!

Swotty shrieked as the brass boy's metal fingers snapped the rope and set him whizzing down the slope.

WAAAH! I'LL SINK! I'LL BE DROWNED!

The slope was short but steep, and the runaway rotter was going like a train when he shot off the bank.

NO-O-O-O! HELP! I'LL GO RIGHT TO THE BOTTOM!

SPLASH!

HAW-HAW! WHAT A FUNNY PLACE TO HAVE A BATH.

Charley and his pals gathered around and laughed themselves hoarse. The water was only inches deep, but Swotty had had the fright of his life. They cut him free and let him stagger off home.

THE SKINNY DRIP HAS TAKEN A DIP!

Charley and his chums couldn't let all the grub they had collected for Swotty's ransom go to waste. They scoffed the lot themselves — and who could wish for a better victory feast?

HO-HO! I'M QUITE GLAD YOU MADE US WORK IN LUIGI'S SHOP NOW, BRASSNECK! THIS ICE CREAM IS SUPER.

A PLEASURE, LADS, BUT I DON'T REMEMBER DOING IT!

YEAH! AND THANKS FOR PINCHING THESE DELICIOUS PIES FROM MY MUM!

GANG HUT

WHAT A SMASHING END TO AN EXCITING DAY!

THE BOY FROM LILLIPUT

BEN LOYAL had been the first visitor to the lost land of Lilliput for 250 years, since Gulliver's famous visit, in fact, and just look what he brought back to Britain with him! Ten tiny men from Lilliput, none more than six inches tall!

Very little had changed in their country over the years They still wore their clothes in the style of olden times, and every man carried a sword. No wonder they were fascinated by the sights of modern Britain!

Ben was staying with one of his chums for a few days, and the two boys were having great fun, for Ben's tiny warriors made the best toy soldiers any boy ever had. Toy soldiers who could talk and walk and could even knock down whole armies of wooden soldiers by firing toy cannon at them!

The game was broken up when Ben and Tony remembered they had some shopping to do for Tony's Mum. The toys were stowed away and the boys set off.

KEEP OUT OF MISCHIEF NOW, MEN. I DON'T WANT TO FIND THE HOUSE IN A MESS WHEN WE GET BACK.

The Lilliputians obeyed. They were sitting around chatting when all of a sudden a big piece of coal rolled out of the fire, broke to bits on the tiles and showered blazing chunks on to the rug near the little men.

Action stations! As the rug began to smoulder, some of the Lilliputians rushed for the fireside shovel. It took three of them to carry it!

HURRY! WE MUST TRY TO SCOOP THOSE COALS UP!

They tried—but the shovel was too big and unwieldy, and in the end heat and smoke drove them back.

LEAVE IT, MEN! WE'LL ATTACK IT FROM ABOVE!

THAT'LL DO THERE, MEN! HERE WE COME!

The rest of the little men had scrambled up to the table-top, where they pushed the big milk jug towards the edge.

Mounted on the shoulders of brawny Bolgo, Marsa began to spoon the milk down on to the burning rug.

A spoonful at a time was doing little good. The jug would have to be tipped over. Marsa and the muscular Bolgo began to push with all their strength.

PUSH IT UP AGAINST US, AND IT WILL TIP OVER AND SPILL IN THE RIGHT DIRECTION.

But the jug was too heavy. In desperation Bolgo charged at it with Marsa seated on his shoulders like a knight of old, using a fork for a lance.

THAT'S DONE IT!

Triumph! The rug was soaked, and the flames died in a hiss of steam and smoke.

The room was so smoky that it brought tears to the tiny men's eyes. A window stood ajar, so some of the Lilliputians clambered up and shoved it wide open.

CAREFUL! WATCH THE PARROT DOESN'T FLY OUT!

Opening that window was going to cause no end of trouble for the Lilliputians. For as the smoke billowed out, it was spotted by Skip Jones, a passing errand boy.

GOLLY! IT LOOKS AS IF THAT HOUSE IS ON FIRE!

When he reached the window, Skip saw there was no longer any danger from fire. But the gleam in his eye told the Lilliputians that here was plenty of danger for them!

REAL LIVE TOY SOLDIERS! HEY, DON'T RUN AWAY!

Skip clambered through the window. And the little men rushed to take up a defensive position — inside the parrot's cage!

The parrot's cage was now a fortress, bristling with tiny swords. And the Lilliputians made ready to hold out in it to the last.

OH, BOY! I COULD HAVE SUPER FUN WITH YOU LOT!

STAND BACK, BOY! OUR SWORDS ARE SHARP!

But that cage turned out to be a trap for the little men, for it wasn't fixed to the table as they thought. Skip simply picked it up and made off with it!

It was too heavy to carry far, so Skip hung it up, then tried to open the door. But all these swords flashing through the bars made him draw back.

YEEOW! YOU LITTLE DEMONS! YOU'VE SLASHED MY HAND!

Skip was a crafty lad, though. He yanked a tablecloth from the washing line and spread it out below the cage.

One quick tug and Skip pulled out the sliding bottom of the cage. The surprised Lilliputians were left without a floor to stand on, and down they tumbled.

I'VE GOT YOU NOW!

The little men landed in a heap, and before they could get their breath back, Skip bundled them all up in the cloth.

The Lilliputians had no chance. In a higgledy-piggledy bunch they were slung over Skip's shoulder in the twinkling of an eye!

I'D BETTER GET AWAY FROM HERE BEFORE ANYONE COMES!

But even as Skip made off with them, the tiny warriors were not as helpless as Skip thought. Marsa used his trusty blade to cut a slash in the cloth.

He wriggled out and began stealthily to climb up towards Skip's head. Would the boy feel the movement and spoil the little man's plan?

The point of the sword, jabbing into its jaw, made the dog yelp and brought it up short. The brave little warrior had gained a precious few seconds for his companions to reach safety.

BRAVELY DONE, MARSA! HURRY NOW!

But the dog was thoroughly enraged, for the "fortress" now occupied by the Lilliputians was its own kennel. Snarling, it launched itself at the tiny men.

The kennel bristled with swords, and two more jabs in the muzzle made the dog flinch. It yelped and whined and barked—but thought twice about poking its head inside the kennel again!

The boys dashed out into the garden to rescue the Lilliputians. And the little warriors weren't half grateful!

What a tale the Lilliputians had to tell. And far from being angry at the mess they had made, Tony's Mum and Dad were full of praise for the little men's heroism in fighting the fire. As a reward they all got specially-big helpings of their evening meal — and if they quarrelled over the choicest bits, well, that showed they were just as human as the big people around them!

P.C. BIG EARS

WILLIE WILEY AND LARRY LIGHTFINGER ARE BEING RELEASED FROM JAIL TODAY, BIG EARS! KEEP AN EAR ON THEM AND MAKE SURE THEY DON'T GET UP TO ANY MISCHIEF!

I'LL DO THAT, SARGE!

IT WAS THANKS TO MY SUPER HEARING THAT THOSE TWO WERE LOCKED UP!

OUTSIDE THE JAIL—

THERE'S THAT BIG-EARED BOBBY WHO NABBED US, LARRY!

HE WON'T CATCH US AGAIN, THANKS TO THE PLAN WE WORKED OUT WHILE WE WERE INSIDE!

I'LL BE ON THE LISTEN FOR YOU TWO!

OH, YOU WON'T HEAR US PLOTTING ANY MORE CRIMES, BIG EARS!

HEE-HEE!

LATER—

THERE ARE THOSE TWO ROGUES! I'LL LISTEN IN AND FIND OUT WHAT THEY'RE UP TO!

FUNNY! I'M LISTENING AS HARD AS I CAN, BUT I STILL CAN'T HEAR A WORD! I'LL HAVE TO MOVE CLOSER.

TWITCH!

TWITCH!

WOW! THEIR LIPS ARE MOVING, BUT I STILL CAN'T HEAR A THING!

SILENCE!

OH, DEAR! I'D BETTER SEE A DOCTOR! THERE MUST BE SOMETHING WRONG WITH MY EARS!

AT THE DOCTOR'S—

THERE'S NOTHING WRONG WITH YOUR EARS, BUT IF YOU'RE WORRIED ABOUT GOING DEAF, WHY DON'T YOU LEARN TO LIP-READ?

LIP-READING?

THAT'S IT—WILLIE AND LARRY MUST HAVE LEARNT TO *LIP-READ!*

SURGERY

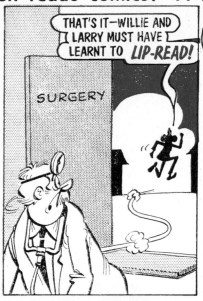

AT THE LIBRARY—

I'LL TAKE THIS ONE—AND DO YOU HAVE ANYTHING ON LIP-READING?

CERTAINLY, SIR!

MUCH LATER THAT NIGHT—

I THINK I'VE MASTERED LIP-READING. NOW TO GET ON WITH THIS!

NEXT DAY—

THERE ARE THE VILLAINS AGAIN—BUT THIS TIME I'LL BE ABLE TO LIP-READ WHAT THEY'RE SAYING!

SILENCE!

SO THAT'S IT! THEY'RE GOING TO RAID BROWN'S BANK TONIGHT! WELL, I'LL BE READY FOR THEM!

THAT EVENING—

TAKEN UP PHOTOGRAPHY, BIG EARS?

YOU COULD SAY THAT, SARGE—I'M GOING TO SNAP SOME VILLAINS!

IN THE BANK—

LOTS OF LOVELY LOLLY!

AND NO BIG EARS TO WORRY ABOUT!

KORKY THE CAT

CAN WE ADOPT THE KOALA BEAR AS OUR SCHOOL MASCOT, KORKY?

SURE YOU CAN!

ZOO

I BET HE WINS OUR SCHOOL COMPETITION TO FIND THE BEST MASCOT.

WE DON'T WANT THAT SILLY LOOKING ANIMAL AS A MASCOT!

SCRAM!

THE ROTTEN BULLIES! THEY THREW THINGS AT OUR MASCOT AND SCARED HIM SO MUCH THAT HE RAN AWAY AND NOW WE CAN'T FIND HIM!

IS THAT SO? WELL, LEAVE IT TO ME. I'LL FIND HIM AND PAY THESE BULLIES BACK AS WELL.

SOMEBODY SAID YOU FELLOWS SCARED AWAY A VALUABLE KOALA BEAR. WELL, THERE'S A BIG REWARD FOR FINDING HIM.

IS THAT SO?

WHAT ARE WE WAITING FOR?

PRESENTLY—

HEY, FELLAS, LOOK! THERE HE IS—UP IN THAT TREE!

THERE'S EVEN A DANGLING ROPE! WE CAN CLIMB UP AND GET HIM!

GURR! THAT'S WHAT I THINK OF YOUR IDEA, CLOTT!

STAMP! CRUSH!

I'VE GOT ANOTHER IDEA. FIRST WE'LL FILL THIS BIG PLASTIC BAG WITH BLACK PAINT.

BLACK

LAC

I'VE TAKEN THE BACK END OFF THE BARREL OF THIS OLD CANNON. NOW TO FIX THE BAG OF PAINT IN POSITION.

HEY! WHAT NONSENSE IS GOING ON HERE? JUST WAIT TILL I TELL COLONEL GRUMBLY!

WE'D BETTER CLEAR OFF BEFORE THE COLONEL COMES!

I'VE GOT A BETTER PLAN! FETCH A LADDER AND WE'LL GET SOME SOOT FROM THE CHIMNEY OF THE COLONEL'S HUT.

WE'LL STEADY THE LADDER FOR YOU, CLOTT.

WOW!

SQUAWK!

FLUTTER!

HELP! I'VE LOST MY BALANCE. AARGH!

OOYAH!

OUCH!

CRASH!

WHAT'S THAT FUNNY NOISE UP MY CHIMNEY?

EEK!

You can weasely tell because they are stoatly different!

WINKER WATSON

WINKER WATSON was a wizard. Not the kind of wizard who casts magic spells, although sometimes his tricks left the Masters at Greytowers School spellbound.

No, Winker was a wizard at wangling. If ever any of Winker's mates in the Third Form wanted to skip prep, or to sneak off to the cinema, or to dodge some punishment, it was Winker to whom they turned. He could wangle it! In fact, he was the champion wangler of all time.

Today was one of those days when some super wangling was going to be necessary. Winker knew it when he heard Mr Creep, the nasty Third Form Master, spring an unpleasant surprise.

COLLECT IN THE EXERCISE BOOKS, WATSON. I'M GIVING THE CLASS A TEST—AND I DON'T WANT ANY FUNNY BUSINESS GOING ON.

YESSIR, MR CREEP, SIR! HAND IT OVER, TROTTY— YOU'RE NOT TO BE TRUSTED!

OOH! LOOK WHO'S TALKING!

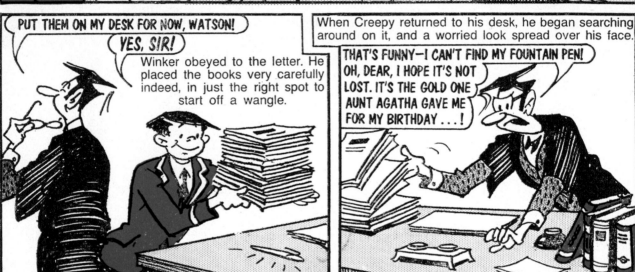

PUT THEM ON MY DESK FOR NOW, WATSON!

YES, SIR!

Winker obeyed to the letter. He placed the books very carefully indeed, in just the right spot to start off a wangle.

When Creepy returned to his desk, he began searching around on it, and a worried look spread over his face.

THAT'S FUNNY—I CAN'T FIND MY FOUNTAIN PEN! OH, DEAR, I HOPE IT'S NOT LOST. IT'S THE GOLD ONE AUNT AGATHA GAVE ME FOR MY BIRTHDAY . . . !

COME HERE, WATSON! DID YOU TAKE MY GOLD PEN FROM MY DESK?

ME, MR CREEP, SIR? OF COURSE NOT, SIR. SEARCH ME IF YOU LIKE!

Creepy was so suspicious, he did just that. He made Winker turn out his pockets.

No pen there! So Creepy set about turning the whole classroom upside down. Talk about hunt the thimble!

OH, DEAR, DO HURRY UP AND FIND IT, BOYS, OR WE WON'T HAVE TIME FOR THE TEST BEFORE THE BELL GOES!

HEE-HEE! THAT'S WHAT WE'RE HOPING!

Boodle was really angry at Winker for showing him up.

GRRR! YOU BEAST, WATSON! YOU SPOILT MY TRICK DELIBERATELY BECAUSE IT WAS BETTER THAN ANY YOU KNOW!

BETTER, BOODLE? LOOK, LET'S BOTH PUT ON A CONJURING SHOW ON SATURDAY AND GET THE HEAD AND CREEPY TO JUDGE WHO'S BEST.

Boodle had so much money that it was no surprise to Winker when presently he spied Jenks, Boodle's manservant, unloading piles of brand new conjuring kits from the millionaire's posh car.

BAH! IT'S ALL VERY WELL FOR MASTER ROBIN TO BUY ALL THIS STUFF—BUT IT'S ME WHO HAS TO LUG IT UP TO HIS ROOM!

GOSH! BOODLE'S MANSERVANT HAS GOT HIS HANDS FULL, WINKER.

I'VE GOT AN IDEA, TROTTY. I'M GOING TO OFFER TO HELP HIM!

THANKS, YOUNG WATSON. I COULD DO WITH SOME HELP.

ANYTHING TO OBLIGE, MR JENKS. I'LL CARRY THIS TABLE AND TOP HAT FOR A START.

Jenks didn't know about the challenge, or he might not have been so pleased to accept Winker's help!

It wasn't far to Boodle's private room, but it was a bit farther the way Winker decided to go!

WAIT FOR ME, TROTTY. I JUST WANT TO NIP IN HERE.

OUT OF BOUNDS

PANTRY

Boodle was delighted with his new equipment, and set out to show his manservant how well he could use it.

SIT THERE, JENKS, AND I WILL AMAZE YOU BY PRODUCING A LIVE WHITE RABBIT FROM THIS HAT ...

But Winker's hand had been in that hat first!

AAGH!

JOLLY CLEVER, MASTER ROBIN, BUT IT'S NOT WHITE, AND IT'S JOLLY WELL DEAD!

Boodle was so terribly angry that he plunged his hand straight back into the hat without thinking.

GURR! I BET SOMEBODY HAS BEEN TAMPERING WITH THIS! I'LL TRY AGAIN . . .

BETTER LUCK THIS TIME, MASTER ROBIN!

But Boodle's luck was no better. In fact, it was worse!

YEOWL!

SNAP!

THAT MAKES A CHANGE, MASTER ROBIN—A MOUSETRAP!

Boodle's troubles weren't over yet. As he was being doctored by Jenks, an angry voice could be heard from outside.

LET ME PUT A BANDAGE ON YOUR FINGER, MASTER ROBIN—ER, SORRY I LAUGHED. I THOUGHT THAT WAS MEANT TO HAPPEN!

HEY! WHOSE WHITE RABBITS ARE THESE IN MY GARDEN?

OH, DEAR! I BET THEY'RE MINE!

The bellows of rage were coming from Jarvis, the janitor. The rabbits which should have been in Boodle's hat were eating the janitor's lettuce!

HURRY UP AND CATCH THEM, OR I'LL REPORT YOU TO THE HEADMASTER!

OO-ER! COME HERE, SNOWY!

With Boodle out of the way, Winker and his pal Tim Trott had a great chance to raid the millionaire's room.

COME ON, TROTTY, LET'S SEE WHAT TUCK BOODLE'S GOT HIDDEN AWAY.

It seemed that Boodle must have been pretty hungry, however, for no food was in sight.

NONE ON THE TABLE, WINKER. HE MUST HAVE GOT IT ALL WELL HIDDEN.

WE'LL FIND IT, TROTTY! I'LL LOOK UNDER THE BED AND YOU LOOK IN THAT CUPBOARD.

HOORAY! I'VE FOUND SOME! HEY, WHERE ARE YOU?

Winker turned to show off the pies and cream cakes he had discovered—but Trotty had vanished!

INSIDE THE CUPBOARD, WINKER!

Where the dickens was he? He was still absent—but his voice wasn't!

DON'T FOOL ABOUT, TROTTY—THE CUPBOARD IS BARE!

OTHER SIDE, WINKER!

The secret was revealed. The cupboard was really two cupboards. Put a man in one, turn it round, open it up, and Hey Presto! No man!

IT'S A SPECIALLY-MADE MAGICIAN'S CABINET, WINKER.

WELL, I'M BLOWED!

Boodle had certainly spared no expense in his bid to be a better magician than Winker.

Winker couldn't hope to win a contest against someone using posh equipment like this. So he set out to do what he was best at—wangling!

YOU KEEP GUARD OUTSIDE BOODLE'S DOOR AND I'LL GET THE JANITOR'S TOOL BOX AND MAKE ONE OR TWO ALTERATIONS TO BOODLE'S TRICK CUPBOARD!

HURRY THEN, WINKER!

A few hours before the contest was due to start, Boodle set out all his fancy gear on the stage of the school hall. He was being his usual boastful self, too.

YOU DON'T STAND A CHANCE, WATSON— JUST LOOK AT ALL THE MAGIC EQUIPMENT I'VE GOT!

POOH! SO WHAT BOODLE? I'M SO JOLLY GOOD, I DON'T NEED ANY OF THAT JUNK! SEE YOU LATER!

Boodle practised all his tricks, but when he left to don his best blazer, Winker did a spot of rearranging.

THERE'S NOBODY ABOUT, SO NOW'S MY CHANCE TO MOVE HIS DISAPPEARING CABINET TO THE SPOT ON THE STAGE WHERE I WANT IT TO BE!

The show began, and Boodle's act was really something. The best trick was the cupboard one, and he kept that till the end.

FOR MY FINAL BIT OF REAL MAGIC I'LL NEED A VOLUNTEER FROM THE AUDIENCE . . .

PSST, MR CREEP, SIR! YOU'RE ONE OF THE JUDGES, SO WHY DON'T YOU GO AND HELP BOODLE, AND SEE HOW GOOD HE REALLY IS?

Wily Winker! If he was to beat Boodle, everything depended upon whether Creepy would step forward.

He did! Boodle was as pleased as punch that a Master had volunteered. Now he'd show Watson!

OO, THANK YOU, MR CREEP, SIR. NOW IF YOU'LL JUST STEP INTO THE MAGIC CABINET . . .

Boodle slammed the cupboard shut, and he was so carried away by his own cleverness that he didn't even hear those noises that should have told him all was perhaps not well.

. . . I'LL SAY A FEW MAGIC WORDS FIRST . . .

YEEOWL!

SLAM!

CRASH!

Boodle screened the cupboard from the audience, then revolved it. The trick was a huge success. Most of the lads hoped Boodle couldn't bring Creepy back!

HEY, PRESTO! MR CREEP HAS VANISHED!

HOORAY!

JOLLY GOOD, BOODLE!

BULLY BEEF AND CHIPS

I'LL HAVE SOME GOOD FUN WITH THIS FALSE NOSE!

TOYS

NOW YOU'LL NEED A DOCTOR TO FIX YOUR NOSE!

YEEAHOO!

THWACK!

TWANG!

GURR!

THROB!

YOUR NOSE WILL SWELL UP, AND YOU WON'T BE ABLE TO WEAR THE FALSE ONE!

SO I'LL TAKE IT!

HEY!

SNATCH!

GURR! I'VE HAD ENOUGH! GIVE IT BACK TO ME AT ONCE!

STRETCH!

OKAY—HERE YOU ARE!

Claude HOPPER

THOSE NEW BOOTS I'VE BOUGHT YOU ARE TERRIBLY SQUEAKY, CLAUDE. PERHAPS IF YOU WALK AROUND A BIT THE SQUEAK WILL DISAPPEAR.

OKAY, DAD!

CREAK!

CREAK!

CRUMBS! WHAT'S THAT NOISE? THE PLANK MUST BE CREAKING! I'D BETTER JUMP OFF BEFORE IT BREAKS!

CREAK!

CREAK!

CONCERT
BRASS BAND
NEXT MONDAY

PASTE

UGH!

SPLOSH!

GURR! IT WAS YOUR BOOTS THAT WERE CREAKING!

HEE-HEE! I'D BETTER SCRAM!

I CAN HEAR THE DUCKS QUACKING LIKE MAD! ARE YOU ANNOYING THEM?

CREAK!

CREAK!

WOW! HE'S TRIPPED OVER MY FOOT!

TRIP!

IT'S YOU WHO ARE ANNOYING THEM! HO-HO!

QUACK!

QUACK!

CREAK!

BAH! MY PIG MUST HAVE GOT OUT! I CAN HEAR IT SNORTING OVER THE WALL!

CREAK!

I MUST CATCH IT BEFORE IT GETS MILES AWAY!

P.C. BIG EARS

HERE YOU ARE, BIG EARS—THE KEY OF YOUR OWN LITTLE PANDA CAR! MAYBE IT'LL HELP YOU CATCH THE GANG OF CAR THIEVES WORKING AROUND HERE.

IT CERTAINLY WILL, SARGE!

HEE-HEE! THIS BEATS BEING ON THE BEAT— HEY! WHAT'S THIS MY KEEN EARS HEAR?

THAT GANG HAS STOLEN MY JOHNNIE'S CAR!

HERE WE ARE—WHICH WAY DID THEY GO, MADAM?

ACROSS THE RAILWAY!

I'LL HAVE TO CONTINUE ON FOOT! CAN'T WASTE TIME WAITING TILL THE GATES OPEN!

IT'S A SUPER CAR!

AHA! THEY'RE ROUND THIS CORNER!

I HEARD YOU! NOW WHERE'S THE STOLEN VEHICLE? GOSH—A BUNCH OF KIDS!

ERK! THE BOBBY'S AFTER US! CHUCK AWAY THE CAR!

EEYARRGH!

CRASH!

BAH! IT WAS A TOY CAR—AND I'VE WRECKED IT!

MEANWHILE—

THERE'S NOBODY ABOUT—WE CAN GET A LOT OF USEFUL SPARE PARTS FROM THIS CAR!

RIGHT, YOU GET CRACKING, AND I'LL TELL THE REST OF THE LADS!

I'LL HAVE THIS!

GERROFF— THAT'S MINE!

SORRY, MADAM—I BUSTED YOUR SON'S TOY—ERK! LOOK AT MY CAR!

SERVES YOU RIGHT, YOU CLUMSY COP!

AT THE POLICE STATION—

ER—MY CAR'S BEEN STOLEN, SARGE—BIT BY BIT, RIGHT DOWN TO THE SHELL!

WHAT?

FANCY BITS OF A POLICE CAR BEING STOLEN! BACK ON THE BEAT, YOU BRAINLESS BUFFOON!

SO—

HEY, WHAT'S GOING ON IN THAT GARAGE? I KNOW EVERY PART OF MY CAR BY THE SOUND— AND THAT SOUNDS LIKE A BIT OF MY ENGINE!

GOT YOU, YOU ROGUES!

ERK!

HERE WE ARE! TWO VILLAINS NICKED AND TWO BITS OF MY CAR RECOVERED! MY KEEN EARS WILL HELP ME GET THE REST OF THE GANG—AND THE CAR!

SOON—

HERE'S ANOTHER ONE, SARGE!

WELL DONE, BIG EARS! YOU'VE GOT ALL THE BITS OF YOUR CAR BACK, AND NABBED EVERY CAR THIEF IN TOWN!

WUN TUN AND TOO TUN

THE CHINESE SPIES

ROYAL AIR FORCE BASE

IF WE HAD POLICE UNIFORMS, WE COULD MARCH STLAIGHT INTO SECLET BLITISH BASE! HERE COMES A POLICEMAN! YOU JUMP INTO RIVER, TOO TUN, AND I'LL GLAB HIS UNIFORM WHEN HE DIVES IN TO SAVE YOU!

ME? AW, OKAY, WUN TUN!

RIVER

HELPEE! SAVE MY DLOWNING FLIEND!

EH?

HELPEE, QUICKLY!

DON'T WORRY! I'LL SAVE HIM! GOOD! ME HELPEE YOU TO UNDLESS!

WHAT'S THE GAME? TAKE YOUR HANDS OFF ME!

GLOOB!

HELPEE! ME CAN'T SWIM!

MY GOODNESS! WHAT HAVE I DONE? I MUST GO IN AND SAVE HIM!

MEANWHILE FURTHER ALONG THE BANK TOO TUN SCRAMBLES ASHORE

HOLD ON! I'M COMING!

WUN TUN CAN'T PINCHEE THE POLICE UNIFORM NOW, SO ME PINCHEE IT INSTEAD!

BAH! THE UNIFORM IS A TLIFLE TOO LONG.. ME SOON FIXEE THAT WITH MY KNIFEE!

PRESENTLY HALT RIGHT THERE, MATEY. WHERE DO YOU THINK YOU'RE GOING?

R.A.F. BASE ENTRANCE

IT'S OKAY, PAL! ME A POLICEMAN!

WHAT POLICE?—THE PEKIN POLICE!

EEK! HOW HE KNOW ME NO BLITISH POLICEMAN?

THE BOBBY FINDS HIS ABANDONED UNIFORM GRR! LOOK WHAT THOSE YELLOW PERILS HAVE DONE! I'LL TEAR THEM APART THE NEXT TIME I SEE THEM!

CLUMBS! METHINKS IT WOULD BE UNWISE TO TLY TO GET INTO SECLET BLITISH BASE AGAIN TODAY, TOO TUN!

I AGLEE, WUN TUN! LET'S GO HOME FOR TEA!

DESPERATE DAN

SLAM

OOF!

THUD

I HEARD A GROAN! THAT GUY MUST HAVE BEEN SLOW GETTING HIS FOOT OUT OF THE WAY—

HEY! WHAT'S HAPPENED HERE?

TUG

THAT LOW DOWN SNEAK THIEF MUST HAVE PINCHED THE DOOR KNOB OFF THE OUTSIDE! I'LL GIVE HIM DOOR KNOBS!

TUG

COME BACK OR I'LL—

OHH! THERE YOU ARE!

YAH!

GOOD, I'VE GOT MY DOOR KNOB BACK! NOW BEAT IT BEFORE I GET ANGRY!

B-BUT! OH, WELL—ER— Y-YES, MR DAN.

DRAT! LOOK WHAT I'VE DONE TO MY DOOR!

SAY, DAN, WHY DON'T YOU GET A REVOLVING DOOR?

IT WOULDN'T BREAK HOWEVER HARD YOU SLAMMED IT.

PLEASE TURN OVER TWO PAGES FOR CONTINUATION

THERE! THAT'S GOT RID OF THEM! *OOPS!* I'VE KICKED SO HARD MY BOOT'S COME OFF.

WHOOOSH

BOOT

CRASH

EEYOW!

LOOK AT THAT! SOMEONE'S BOOTED THE POSTMASTER!

WHOOOSH

WHUMP

YOU BIG OAF! I COULD HAVE THE LAW ON YOU FOR THAT!

WELL, IT JUST SERVES YOU RIGHT, MR POSTMASTER.

MAYBE YOU'LL TEACH YOUR POSTIES TO STOP BASHING PEOPLE'S DOORS AND DELIVERING THE WRONG MAIL.

OH, DEAR!

SAY, DAN, THAT'S A RIGHT MESS YOU'VE MADE OF YOUR NEW DOOR. COME WITH ME, I KNOW JUST THE PLACE WHERE YOU MIGHT GET THE RIGHT KIND OF DOOR FOR YOUR HOUSE.

AND SO—

HAULIERS

MUST BE SOME DOOR DAN'S HAVING FITTED. THEY'RE HAVING TO LIFT IT INTO POSITION WITH A CRANE!

No footslogging for the lads, either! The boys of Marsuvia had little space-scooters which they used like Curly had used a bicycle on Earth.

YIPPEE! WAIT FOR ME, JACK!

Curly was still a learner pilot and it was lucky that the tree he hit on take-off was a funny, bendy Marsuvian one and not an English oak!

GOSH! THIS IS BETTER THAN CYCLING ANY DAY!

GOBBLE-GOBBLE!

FULL SPEED AHEAD, CURLY!

But just look at what was following the flying fishermen now!

Curly gulped as the weird Marsuvian monster snapped at his trailing bait.

EEK! A FLYING MONSTER! HELP!

Paralysed with fear, Curly forgot to let go of the rod and was jerked off his scooter.

OOPS! HOLD ON TIGHT TO YOUR ROD, CURLY!

EEYAGH! IT'S GOT ME!

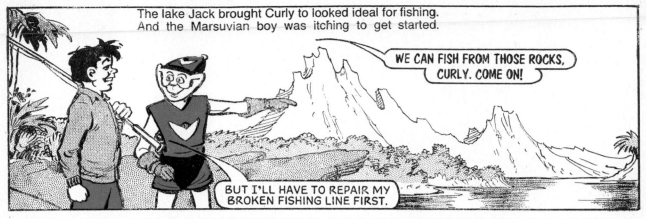

The lake Jack brought Curly to looked ideal for fishing.
And the Marsuvian boy was itching to get started.

WE CAN FISH FROM THOSE ROCKS, CURLY. COME ON!

BUT I'LL HAVE TO REPAIR MY BROKEN FISHING LINE FIRST.

Curly whistled in surprise as Jack peeled a fibre from a creeper-like plant. The thread was very thin, but as strong as a steel wire.

LOOK, YOU CAN USE THIS.

GOSH! I BET MY MUM WOULDN'T MIND ONE OF THESE PLANTS IN THE HOUSE FOR HER SEWING.

Curly showed his pal how to cast, then set about repairing his own line with the fibre.

WISH ME LUCK, CURLY!

HEY! THAT'S QUICK WORK!

Hardly had the bait hit the water when Jack's rod bent and his reel began to scream as line went ripping off it.

OOH! THIS IS EXCITING! IT MUST BE A MONSTER FISH!

Jack Silver held on gamely but the fish was a big one all right. It dived down deep— and the line snapped!

HO-HO! IT MUST HAVE BEEN AS BIG AS THIS TO DO THAT!

BY THE THREE MOONS OF MARSUVIA, I'VE BEEN CHEATED!

The bait was gone too now, but Curly knew how to get more.

WATCH ME CATCH THIS FUNNY-LOOKING THING, JACK.

An outlandish hairy hornet for bait? Jack Silver rocked with laughter!

HOW'S THAT?

TEE, HEE! WHAT'S THE IDEA? ARE YOU GOING TO STING THEM TO DEATH?

But as Curly made his cast and the funny bait hit the water, fish of all shapes and sizes took one look, then fled from the spot.

I DON'T THINK THEY LIKE THAT BAIT OF YOURS, CURLY!

It looked as if the buzzing bait had given the fish a scare. And what happened next left Curly speechless — the fish spread out wing-like fins and flapped up into the air!

HEY! THEY'RE FLYING AWAY!

YOU'VE SCARED THEM OFF, CURLY!

Jack Silver wasn't in the least surprised, however. It was quite common for Marsuvian fish to fly from lake to lake in search of food.

QUICK, CURLY! WE CAN FOLLOW THEM IN OUR SCOOTER!

REALLY?

The boys jumped on board their space-scooter and roared off in pursuit.

EITHER I'M DREAMING OR THIS IS THE CRAZIEST FISHING EXPEDITION EVER!

But when Jack saw where the fish were heading, he groaned. It was a private lake, the property of a greedy landowner.

THAT'S RIGHT, FISHES, FLY INTO MY NICE BIG LAKE!

OH, NO!

Had the boys chased the fish in vain? It seemed so.

CLEAR OFF, YOU TWO! CAN'T YOU SEE THIS IS A PRIVATE LAKE?

Disappointed and angry, the boys took to the air again.

SORRY, CURLY, WE'LL JUST HAVE TO TRY SOMEWHERE ELSE.

HOLD ON THOUGH, JACK! I LEFT MY ROD BACK THERE.

Jack's and Curly's anger doubled when they looked back and saw that the rotten landowner had found the rod and was about to try it himself.

HEY! LOOK! PODGY-FACE HAS NABBED IT!

The man had heard of the fishing rods which had been brought from Earth, and he wasn't long in discovering how to use this one. A bite soon came.

COME ON, LET'S GRAB IT BACK!

I'VE HOOKED SOME-THING ALREADY!

Jack and Curly yelled with delight now, for the catch was a monster, and more than a match for the angler. The huge fish leapt from the water with such force that the man was jerked off his feet and into the air.

HO-HO!

YIPPEE! LOOK HOW STRONG THAT FISH IS!

Splosh! The landowner paid for his nastiness with a ducking in his own lake.

EEYAGH!

Shaking with mirth, Jack brought his scooter down.

HAW-HAW! DON'T WORRY, PODGY! YOU'RE TOO FAT TO DROWN!

WE'D BETTER PULL HIM ASHORE.

HELP!

But the podgy-faced land-owner wanted no help. He flew into a rage and threw a handful of mud hard at Jack.

BAW! YOU HOOLIGANS WERE TO BLAME FOR THAT!

WOW!

GROOGH!

When Jack shook the mud off his face Curly could see he was hopping mad. Suddenly sparks shot from the tips of the Marsuvian boy's gloves. Curly drew back, for he knew what happened when electric sparks flew from these amazing gloves.

GURR! FAT FACE WILL PAY FOR THAT!

WOW!

Boom! Bang! Pop! The little lightning flashes hit the strange sausage-shaped plants growing by the water's edge and made them blow up like firecrackers.

WAH! YOWCH! EEK!

It was too much for Podgy, and he took to his heels.

GOSH! YOU SURE MADE HIM DANCE, JACK!

HELP!

Jack wanted another go at rod fishing now, but Curly had a better plan in mind.

FISHING RODS ARE NO USE FOR THE HUGE FISH HERE. I'LL GO AND FETCH SOMETHING FROM THE SPACE SHIP.

RIGHT!

Leaving Jack to try his luck, Curly revved up the space-scooter and shot off.

WOULDN'T IT BE A LAUGH IF I CAUGHT SOMETHING BEFORE CURLY GOT BACK!

Curly returned minutes later with two bows and an armful of arrows, and he was just in time to see a huge fish wrenching the rod from Jack Silver's grasp.

GIVE UP, JACK! YOU'RE NOT STRONG ENOUGH TO LAND A FISH AS BIG AS THAT—AND NEITHER IS THE ROD!

AW, IT'S NOT FAIR!

Curly's idea was to shoot the fish with bow and arrow, if only they could be made to jump out of the water again.

I KNOW HOW WE CAN DO IT WITH THE HELP OF THAT HOT WATER GEYSER, CURLY!

The boys waited until the spout from the geyser died down, and then they dropped a cake of soap into it.

RIGHT! NOW BRING UP THAT BOULDER, JACK.

QUICKLY! IT MAY START UP AGAIN ANY MOMENT.

The boys barely had time to position a slab of rock across the blow-hole before the geyser spouted and sent them scurrying for cover.

IT'S WORKING, CURLY!

G-GOSH! LET'S GET OUT OF HERE FAST!

What a sight there was now for the boys had placed the rock slab exactly right, and a fantastic cascade of bubbling hot water jetted from the geyser into the lake.

THERE SHE GOES! AND THE BOILING WATER IS FIZZING INTO THE LAKE JUST WHERE WE WANTED IT!

WE'D BETTER GET DOWN TO THE LAKESIDE QUICK.

The stinging hot shower from the geyser did the trick. When those funny fish found themselves in hot water, they couldn't get out of it quickly enough, and Jack and Curly were waiting with arrows strung to their bows, and each picked a fish and let fly.

The monster flying fish made super targets, and the air was so thick with them that Jack and Curly were able to pull in their fish, then use those same arrows to shoot another and another.

They ended up with so many fish that it took two trips to get them all back to the space ship.

Curly had never dreamed of catching fish as big as these, and Jack Silver had never imagined fishing could be such sport. But it was just as well they had made such a super catch, for this adventure had given them monster appetites. They just couldn't wait to get one of those fish fried!

CLAUDE HOPPER

OH, DEAR! ALL THIS WALKING HAS WORN HOLES IN MY SHOES! I'D BETTER GO AND HAVE THEM RE-PAIRED!

WHAT A MONSTER PAIR OF SHOES! IT WILL COST FIVE POUNDS TO REPAIR THEM.

OH, GOSH!

BAH! WHAT A RACKET! WE GET NO PEACE SINCE THAT OPERA SINGER MOVED INTO OUR STREET!

IT'S USELESS TRYING TO SNOOZE IN THE GARDEN! I'LL GO FOR A WALK.

I CAN'T AFFORD TO PAY THAT MUCH!

MEE-YOW!

BOOT REPAIRS

RUBBER STICK-ON SOLES! THESE WOULD BE CHEAPER IF I COULD STRETCH A PAIR OF THEM TO FIT MY SHOES!

I'LL STICK THEM ON IN THE GARDEN SHED!

I'VE SPREAD ON THE GLUE, BUT THE RUBBER TAKES SOME STRETCHING!

WELL, THAT'S ONE DONE. I THINK I'LL PUT THE SHOE ON AND TRY IT OUT.

The SMASHER

EEK! SOMEONE'S PINCHING MY FOOTBALL BOOTS!

STOP, THIEF!

HOLD ON, SMASHER! YOU'RE NOT GOING OUT TO PLAY IN YOUR PYJAMAS!

GRAB

BUT, MA, WE'VE GOT A BIG MATCH AGAINST THE BROWN STREET BRUISERS TODAY.

THAT'S YOUR HARD LUCK—AND DON'T DARE PLAY IN YOUR ORDINARY SHOES!

AFTER BREAKFAST—
I'VE GOT A FEELING THE BRUISERS WERE BEHIND THIS. I'LL GO AND LOOK THEM UP.

SMASHER'S SNOOPING ON US. GET HIM, SNAPPER!

THE BRUISERS HAVE SET THEIR DOG ON ME!

THANK GOODNESS DOGS CAN'T CLIMB TREES!

GROWL!

WOOF!

HO-HO! THIS BRANCH REACHES OVER TO THE OTHER SIDE OF THE FENCE.

GRR! HE'S GETTING AWAY!

WOW! MUD!

TER A CLEAN-UP—
WAS RIGHT. IT WAS ONE OF E BRUISERS WHO PINCHED MY BOOTS. GOOD THING I ROUGHT THIS SOOT BOMB ALONG.

THAT'S IT! CHUCK SMASHER'S BOOTS INTO THE POND.

TAKE THAT!

SWOOSH!

URRGH!

WHACKO!

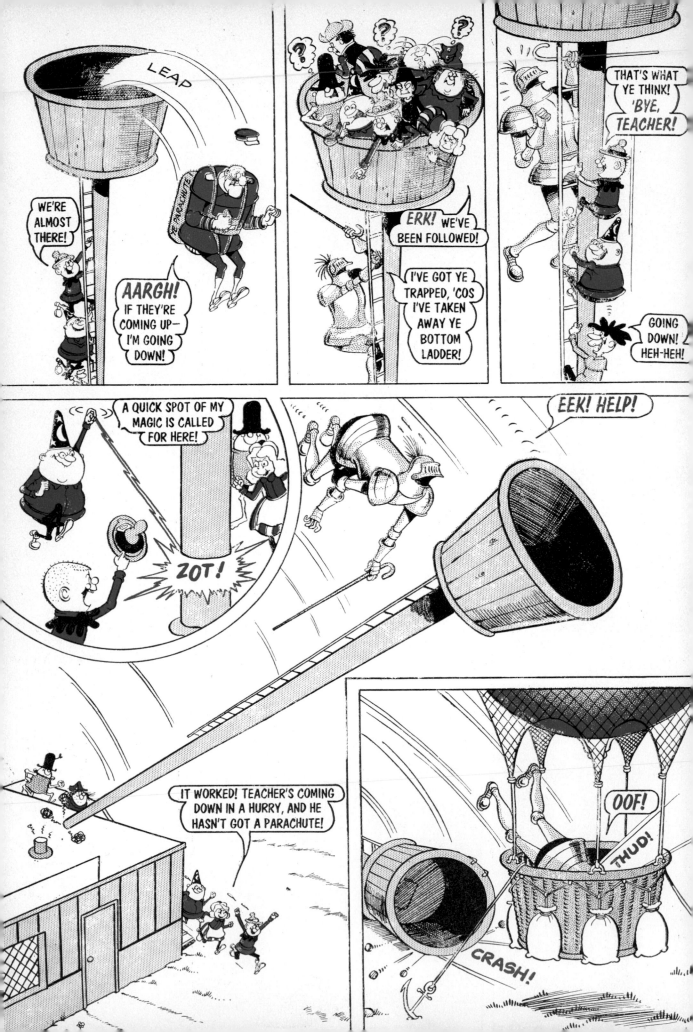

HO-HO! NOW WHILE THEY'RE OUT ON THAT WILD GOOSE CHASE, I'LL SCOFF THE FISH FROM THEIR PLATES!

AND PLANT A FEW OF TOM SCRATCHER'S PAW PRINTS AROUND!

DAB

WE COULDN'T SEE ANYBODY, UNCLE DAN!

HE MUST HAVE VAMOOSED PRETTY FAST!

HEY! SOMEBODY'S PINCHED THE FISH OFF MY PLATE!

AND LOOK AT THE PAWMARKS ON THE TABLE CLOTH!

IT MUST HAVE BEEN THAT ROTTEN MOGGIE OF YOURS, UNCLE DAN!

BUT AFTER DINNER

YOU KNOW, DANNY, I DON'T THINK IT WAS THAT MOGGIE AFTER ALL. UNCLE DAN WOULD NEVER SIT THERE AND WATCH A CAT SCOFFING OUR FISH WHEN HE WAS HUNGRY HIMSELF!

BY CRACKY, YOU'RE RIGHT, KATEY!

I'VE BOUGHT A FEW SAUSAGES FOR MY SUPPER, BUT I'M GONNA LOCK 'EM IN MY BEDROOM OUT OF TOM SCRATCHER'S REACH!

UNCLE DAN'S GONE OUT. NOW'S OUR CHANCE, KATEY! WE'LL BURGLE HIS BEDROOM AND BLAME THE CAT!

BUT HOW? WE HAVEN'T GOT A LADDER, DANNY!